*Learning to read requires many more skills
than just decoding words. This lively, colourful
book based on rhymes, both old and new, is
for young children who are not yet reading
and for many who have just begun.*

*It will encourage them to look closely at
pictures, to spot similarities and differences,
to practise sequencing and anticipation, and
to enjoy the sounds and rhythm of language
while 'reading' the stories told in pictures.*

*On each double-page spread, the artist has
hidden a little ladybird like this:*
Can your child find it?

British Library Cataloguing in Publication Data

Haselden, Mary
    Picture reading rhymes.
    1. English language. Readers
    I. Title   II. Goffe, Toni   III. Series
    428.6
    ISBN 0-7214-1182-7

First edition

Published by Ladybird Books Ltd Loughborough Leicestershire UK
Ladybird Books Inc Auburn Maine 04210 USA

© LADYBIRD BOOKS LTD MCMLXXXIX

Printed in England

picture reading
rhymes

by MARY HASELDEN
illustrated by TONI GOFFE

Ladybird Books

What belongs to each of the nursery rhyme characters?

Little Bo Peep

Mary, Mary
quite contrary

Jack and Jill

The Old Woman
who lived in a shoe

Big brown boots go
Tramp, tramp, tramp.
Little red shoes go
Stamp, stamp, stamp.
Silver slippers go
Trip, trip, trip.
And my two feet go
Skip, skip, skip.

Match the pairs.

*There's a wide eyed owl
With a pointed nose,
Two pointed ears
And claws for his toes.*

*Find six differences in the
bottom picture.*

Look at the pictures and tell the story in the right order.

Incy Wincy spider
Climbed up the water spout.
Down came the rain
And washed the spider out.
Out came the sunshine,
Dried up all the rain.
And Incy Wincy spider
Climbed the spout again.

The Queen of Hearts
She made some tarts
All on a summer's day.
The Knave of Hearts
He stole the tarts
And took them clean away.

Find six jam tarts hidden in the picture.

I'm a little teapot short and stout,
Here's my handle, here's my spout.
When I see the tea cups,
                    hear me shout,
Tip me up and pour me out.

Where does each piece of the teapot go?

Which comes **first** in each row?

Which comes **last** in each row?

Miss Polly had a dolly who was
sick, sick, sick.
So she called for the Doctor to come
quick, quick, quick.
The Doctor came with his bag
and his hat
And he knocked at the door with
a rat, tat, tat.

Put the
pictures in
the right
order.

He looked at the dolly and he
shook his head.
He said, ''Miss Polly put her straight
to bed.''
He wrote on the paper for the
pill, pill, pill.
''I'll be back in the morning with my
bill, bill, bill.''

Say each of these rhymes.

Here are two endings for each rhyme. Which one is correct?

What's different in each pair of pictures?

Early to bed

Early to rise

Will make you healthy, wealthy and wise.

Little Arabella Millar,
    found a woolly caterpillar.
First she put it on her mother.
Then upon her baby brother.
Both said, ''Arabella Millar,
    Take away this caterpillar.''

Tell the story.

Jelly on a plate.
Jelly on a plate.
Wibble, wobble, wibble, wobble,
Jelly on a plate!

Find another

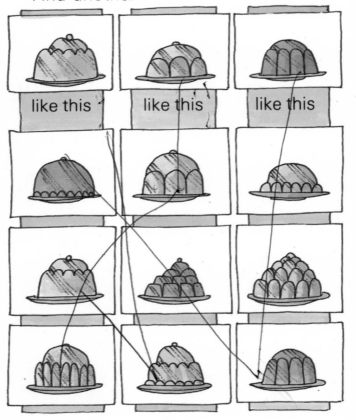

like this   like this   like this

Roses are red,
Violets are blue,
Sugar is sweet
And so are you.

How many red flowers? 5
How many blue flowers? 4

Hey diddle diddle, the cat
and the fiddle,
The cow jumped over the moon.
The little dog laughed to see
such sport,
And the dish ran away with
the spoon.

Talk about the picture.

Where is the frog hiding? *in the flowers*

How many butterflies? *3*

Where do you think the dish and spoon went?

Which child was born on each day?

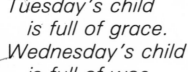

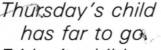

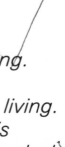

Monday's child
  is fair of face.
Tuesday's child
  is full of grace.
Wednesday's child
  is full of woe.
Thursday's child
  has far to go.
Friday's child
  is loving and giving.
Saturday's child
  works hard for a living.
And the child that is
  born on the Sabbath day,
Is bonny and blithe
  and good and gay.

Point to each person in the right order.

Tinker   Tailor
     Soldier   Sailor
Rich man
          Poor man
Beggarman
          Thief

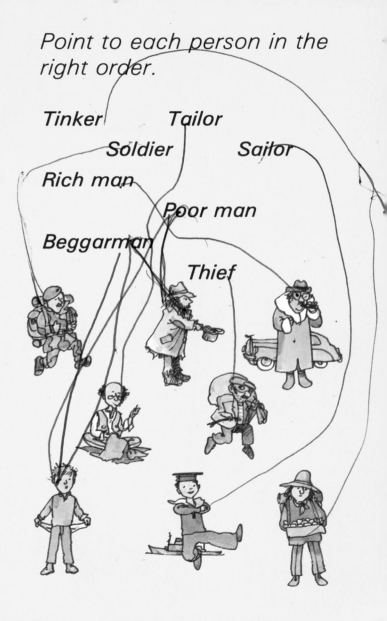

Say these rhymes.
Listen to the sounds.

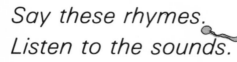

Peter Piper picked a
peck of pickled pepper.
If Peter Piper picked a
peck of pickled pepper
Where's the peck of pickled
pepper
Peter Piper picked?

She sells seashells
on the seashore.
The shells she sells
are seashells I'm sure.

Can you say them very fast?

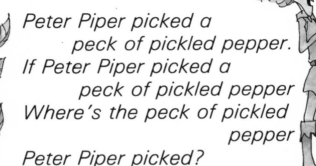

As I was going to St Ives,
I met a man with seven wives;
Each wife had seven sacks,
Each sack had seven cats,
Each cat had seven kittens:
Kittens, cats, sacks and wives,
How many were there going
to St Ives?

Answer – only one, the others were going
somewhere else!